THE WILD LIFE OF ANIMALS

BUSTER BOOKS

EDITED BY SUSANNAH BAILEY
DESIGNED BY JACK CLUCAS
COVER DESIGNED BY JOHN BIGWOOD

For Roly — MB

To Sami, who is so patient. Thanks for always
waiting for me so we can play together — PB

First published in Great Britain in 2023 by
Buster Books, an imprint of Michael O'Mara Books Limited,
9 Lion Yard, Tremadoc Road, London SW4 7NQ

W www.mombooks.com/buster   F Buster Books   T @BusterBooks   O @buster_books

Text and layout © Mike Barfield 2023

Illustrations copyright © Buster Books 2023

A CIP catalogue record for this book is available from the British Library.

ISBN: 978-1-78055-819-6

3 5 7 9 10 8 6 4 2

This book was printed in October 2023 by
Shenzhen Wing King Tong Paper Products Co. Ltd.,
Shenzhen Guangdong, China.

THE WILD LIFE OF ANIMALS

WRITTEN BY MIKE BARFIELD

ILLUSTRATED BY PAULA BOSSIO

CONTENTS

INTRODUCTION

Can you keep a secret? Get ready for a thrilling ride as we reveal the hidden lives of some weird and wonderful animals.

In these pages, you will meet fish, frogs, monkeys, meerkats, lizards, leopards, bats, birds, bugs, bears and a whole host of other animals from different habitats across the globe.

Some swim, some fly, some glide, some crawl — and they range in size from tiny spiders to the mighty blue whale, the largest animal that has ever lived.

As well as colourful comics in which astounding animals talk us through their secret lives, there are 'Wild Style' guides to some of nature's hottest looks, and young animals share their plans for the future in 'When I Grow Up'.

The book is divided into sections based on habitats and lifestyles, but just like a macaroni penguin setting out to sea near the South Pole, you can dive in anywhere and start laughing and learning.

We guarantee, you'll have a really wild time.

WOODS AND FORESTS:
BRANCHES EVERYWHERE

Woods and forests make wonderful homes for animals
that love to live undercover. Trees are the key
to these habitats, offering shade, food and
safe places to live, often above the ground.

Tropical regions have rainforests — lush, leafy places
where it stays warm and wet all year round. Other regions
have temperate forests that are cooler and drier,
where the leaves of trees may change with the seasons.

Over half the world's animal species are said to live in
rainforests, with many new ones still to be discovered.

Here are some forest animals whose
secrets we can now reveal.

WEAVER ANT

Hello! We're weaver ants, living high up in a mango tree in Thailand.

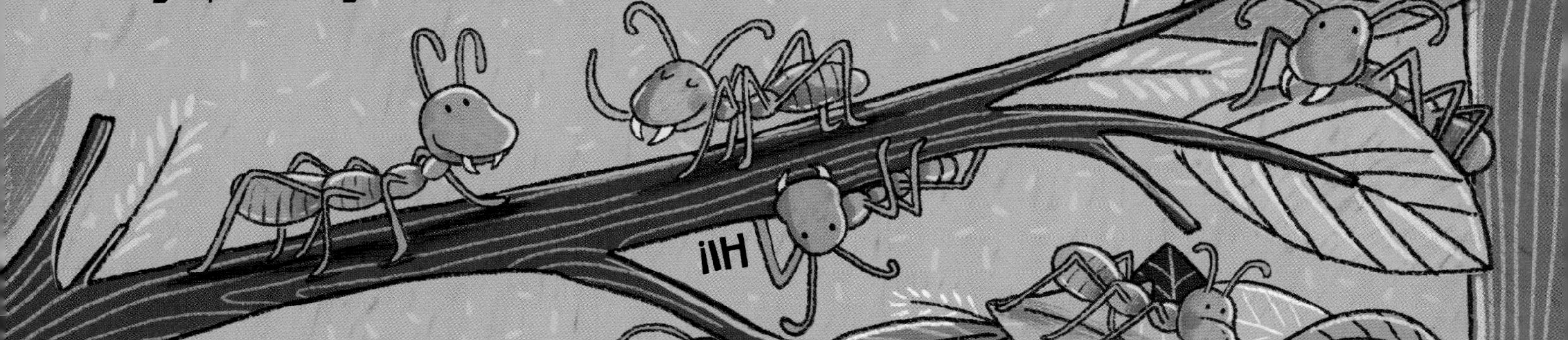

¡IH

This big ball of leaves in the warm sunshine is our home. There's half a million of us in this colony.

THAT'S RIGHT!

THERE ARE!

Some of us are big.

8-MILLIMETRES LONG

Some of us are small.

4-MILLIMETRES LONG

Some of us are only babies (called larvae).

We build our nests by pulling nearby leaves together with our sharp jaws and claws.

Then we glue their edges together with strands of sticky silk.

PULL! TUG!

In fact, this sticky silk is sprayed from the mouths of our own baby ants after we stroke them. They're like little glue bottles!

STROKE!

SQUIRT!

SPRAY!

STICK!

And when we need to connect leaves that are further apart, 'Team Weaver' has a cunning plan.

THIS WILL NEED TEAMWORK.

We form chains to reach leaves and bring them together. Humans call it 'joined-up thinking' — we call it madness! Luckily, we can lift 100 times our body weight.

STRETCH!

WOBBLE!

By working together, we can build lots of new nests across the canopy — some as big as beach balls.

We're only little, but I'd say we're pretty incredible animals.

YOU'RE RIGHT!

THAT'S RIGHT!

THEY ARE!

WE ARE!

AFRICAN GIANT MILLIPEDE

RIPPLE!

SCUTTLE!

Hi! I'm an African giant millipede out for a nice night-time feed on the floor of a forest in Kenya.

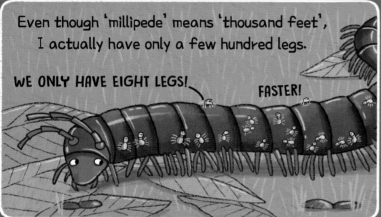

Even though 'millipede' means 'thousand feet', I actually have only a few hundred legs.

WE ONLY HAVE EIGHT LEGS!

FASTER!

Each of my segments — except my head and tail — has two pairs of legs, and lots of mites that come along for the ride.

ONE SEGMENT

WE HELP KEEP THEM CLEAN.

FASTER!

Despite having lots of legs, I don't move very fast. But then my food, dead and rotting plants, doesn't move at all.

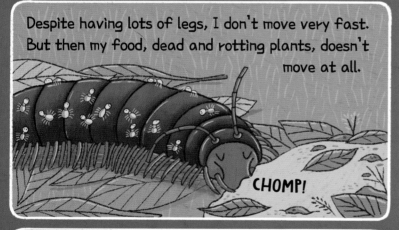

CHOMP!

I can't see very well so I use my legs and antennae to feel around me.

GENET

EEK! PREDATOR!

'Detect and protect' is how I stay alive — circling round and releasing a foul smelling fluid!

PONG!

STINK!

YUCK!

I'M OFF!

LET'S LEG IT!

BYE!

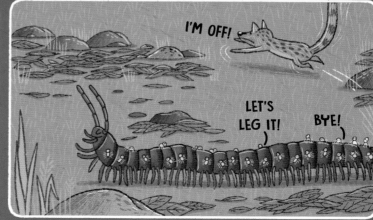

BLACK HOWLER MONKEY

ME

HI! This is me with my mum, resting in the branches of a tree in a rainforest in **BRAZIL** (we do a lot of resting).

I'm part of a group of **15 MONKEYS**. The adult males have black fur while the females and babies are blonde.

HOWL!

WOW!

Who needs an **ALARM CLOCK?** Each morning begins with the adults howling loudly. It's a real scream!

They can be heard up to 5 kilometres away, and apparently it lets other monkeys know to keep away. These trees are ours and I'll be **SHOUTING** ABOUT IT TOO, one day.

Mum carries me about a lot. She **SWINGS** through the branches using her long limbs, staying up in the treetops.

However, we can also use our **LONG TAILS** like an extra hand. I'll be a real **ACROBAT** when I'm bigger.

I'm still getting milk from Mum, but one day I'll eat only leaves. That's why it's hard when the humans cut down our trees. Please leave us lots to eat, or we really will have something to **HOWL** about.

PYGMY HIPPOPOTAMUS

Hello! We're a pair of pygmy hippopotamuses chillin' in a swamp in a forest in Liberia, Western Africa.

We're literally chillin' as being in the water helps keep us cool during the day.

'Pygmy' means small. Compared to our hippo cousins, we're about a quarter of their weight.

ORIGINAL

PYGMY

We're still as heavy as a piano though. Fancy lifting that?

As you can see, our ears, eyes and nostrils are all at the top of our heads.

That's so we can lie low in the water until night-time, more or less undisturbed.

THIS IS A HANDY ISLAND.

JACANA BIRD

SINK!

WALK!

PFFT!

AMATEURS.

Though sometimes we close our ears and noses and go for a stroll underwater.

However, we don't actually swim — instead we just walk along the bottom!

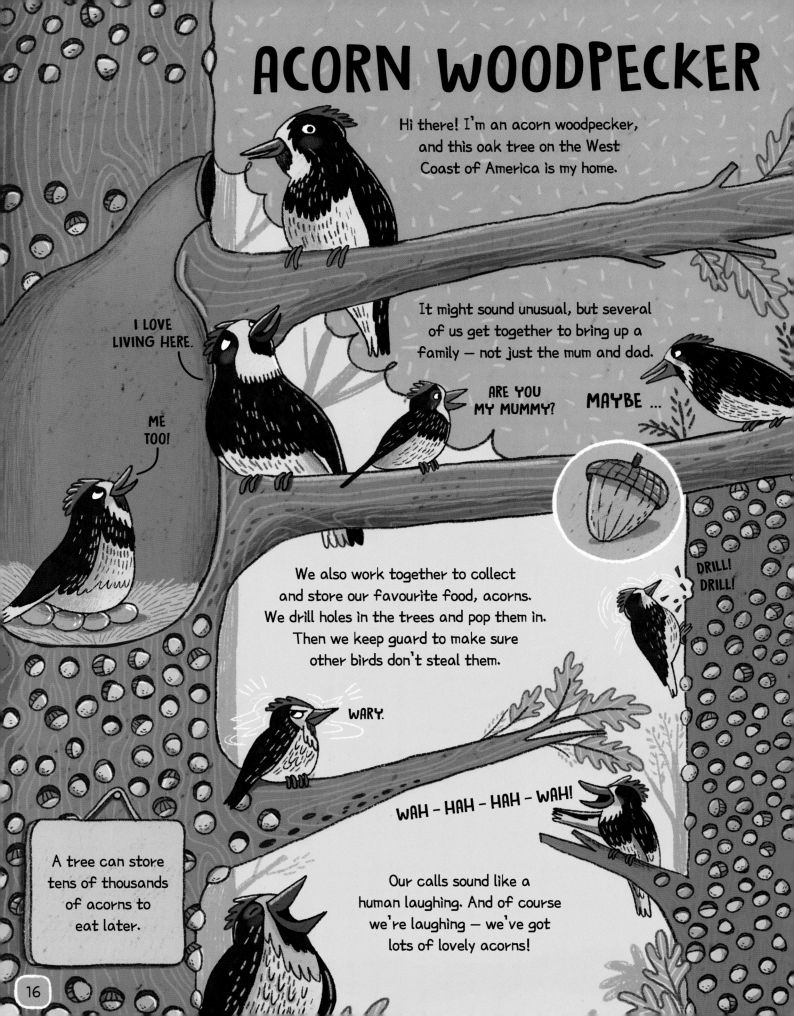

ACORN WOODPECKER

Hi there! I'm an acorn woodpecker, and this oak tree on the West Coast of America is my home.

It might sound unusual, but several of us get together to bring up a family – not just the mum and dad.

I LOVE LIVING HERE.

ME TOO!

ARE YOU MY MUMMY?

MAYBE ...

DRILL! DRILL!

We also work together to collect and store our favourite food, acorns. We drill holes in the trees and pop them in. Then we keep guard to make sure other birds don't steal them.

WARY.

WAH – HAH – HAH – WAH!

Our calls sound like a human laughing. And of course we're laughing – we've got lots of lovely acorns!

A tree can store tens of thousands of acorns to eat later.

WILD STYLE

BRANCHING OUT

From the tallest treetops to the woodland floor, here are some animals that look forest-fabulous!

HIDDEN TREASURE

The okapi of Central Africa is also known as the 'forest giraffe', after its closest living cousin. It has stripy legs for camouflage and a 45-centimetre-long tongue for stripping leaves off trees.

PECKISH?

Great hornbills are named after their huge horn-like beaks which help them reach faraway fruits on trees in Asian rainforests. The seeds then pass through their bodies, and their poo helps spread them into new areas.

BEETLE POWER

Rhinoceros beetles are found on forest floors from Europe to Asia. Just 2-centimetres long, they look like tiny rhinos and can lift over 850 times their body weight. They use this strength to dig holes to hide from danger.

NET THREAT

Found in rainforests in South-East Asia, the reticulated python is named after the net-like pattern of its scales, which help it hide among leaves. At over 6-metres long, it is the world's longest snake and can swallow a whole deer.

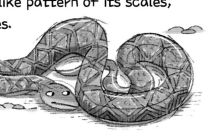

PARADISE TREE SNAKE

Welcome to a forest in the Philippines. I'm a paradise tree snake, and look at me ...

... I'm BEAUTIFUL!

GLIDE!

Sadly, many humans don't like snakes. It might be because some of us slither.

Frankly, I'm not that keen on slithering either. So I climb trees instead.

LIZARD

UH-OH! I'M OFF!

Special scales help me grip the trunk.

GRIP!

Going up!

CLIMB!

I hunt lizards and bats up here.

HIDE!

WHERE DID IT GO?

Oh well, I'll simply look in another tree. I hang by my tail ...

... and jump!

LEAP!

As I fall, I flatten my body to help me fly.

Then I can glide for 10 m or more by 'swimming' through the air.

WIGGLE!

GLIDE!

OOF! Crash landing! But why slither when you can fly?

WHUMP!

GRASSLANDS: GREEN FOR GO!

Grasslands are found on every continent on Earth, except Antarctica where it's just too cold and dry. These wide-open spaces have many different names — steppes, savannahs, plains, pampas, among others — and a huge range of animals call them home.

With few trees and lots of low-growing plants, animals keep themselves safe from predators by hiding in holes or being super-speedy to outrun them. Some animals, such as zebras and giraffes, also form huge herds to confuse hunters.

Here's a grassroots guide to some of this habitat's astounding animals and their super survival secrets.

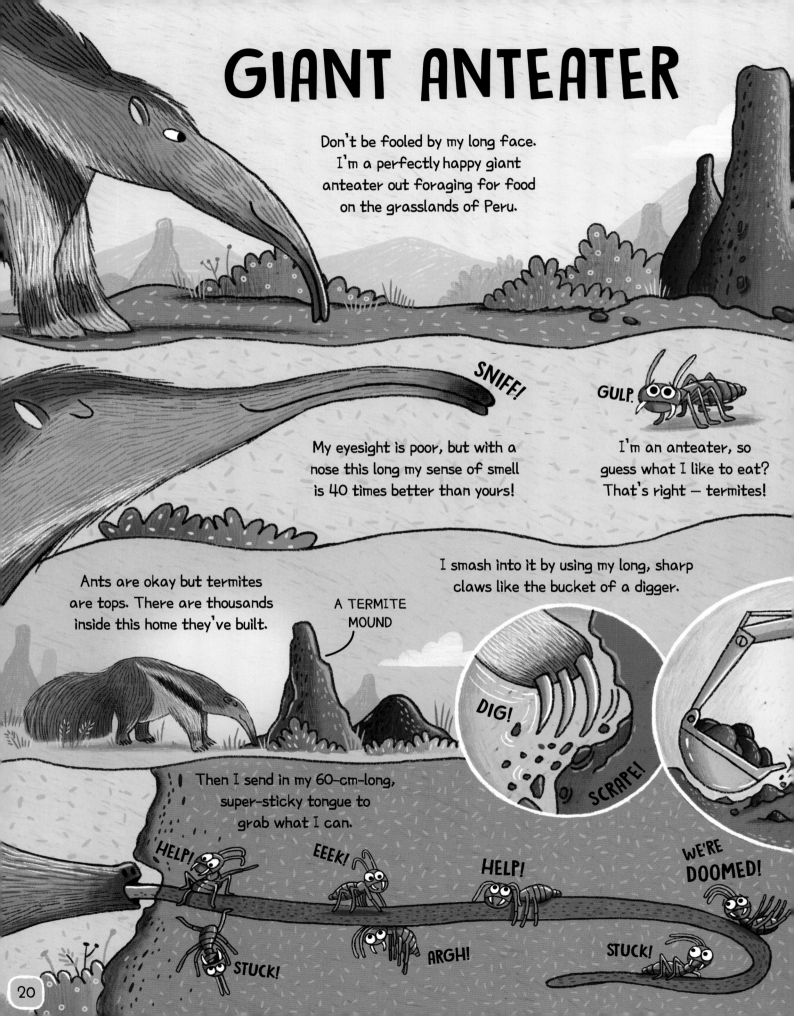

WILD STYLE

OUT TO GRASS

Whether they live on a plain, a prairie or a savannah — these very different animals all come top of their grass!

PICTURE THIS

African wild dogs are also known as 'painted dogs' because of their beautifully marked fur, which may help pack-mates recognize each other.

HAVING A BALL

Found in the Americas, armadillos are the only mammals with a hard shell. They have lots of separate scales and two species of armadillo can curl into a ball to protect themselves.

STAR TURN

The Indian star tortoise has stunning black and gold stars on its shell. These amazing markings may make the tortoise harder to spot when it sits in grass.

LUCKY STRIPES

Zebras have quite easily the strongest look of any African savannah animal. They are actually black with white stripes, not the other way around. The stripes were once thought to confuse lions and cheetahs. Now they are thought to confuse biting flies, as well as keeping zebras feeling (and looking) cool.

WOMBAT

Hey there! Welcome to Australia! The two of us are wombats.

What do you mean 'there's only one of me'?

Look who's hiding in my pouch — my little joey!

HI!

Wombats are marsupials (as are kangaroos). Kangaroos' pouches face forwards, but ours face backwards for a very good reason ...

TELL THEM, MUM!

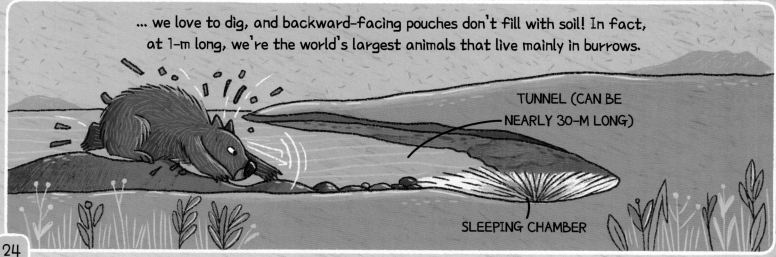

... we love to dig, and backward-facing pouches don't fill with soil! In fact, at 1-m long, we're the world's largest animals that live mainly in burrows.

TUNNEL (CAN BE NEARLY 30-M LONG)

SLEEPING CHAMBER

Us wombats spend two-thirds of our lives in our tunnels, hiding from the hot sun.

SAFE! COOL!

But when the sun goes down, we come up to do our favourite thing: EAT!

SNIFF! SNIFF!

We eat grass ...

YUM! CHEW!

... we eat roots ...

YUM! BITE!

... and we eat bark.

GNAW! YUM!

A meal can take us two weeks to digest.

SNORE!

I'm not sleeping, I'm digesting. Zzzzz!

But the end result is something unique — cube-shaped poos!

2 MM

GREAT — A SQUARE MEAL!

I do 80 to 100 poos every night to mark my territory. Cuboid poos don't roll away!

What do you want to do when you grow up?

SLEEP AND POO LIKE YOU, MA, OF COURSE!

GREAT BUSTARD

FLAP!

It's springtime, high over a wide, grassy plain in North-east China. Get ready for landing! I'm a male great bustard — one of the world's heaviest flying birds!

It's the mating season, and I've come to a very special site known as a lek. And what makes it special?

Female great bustards! I haven't seen them all winter. I'd almost forgotten how small they are compared to us males.

CHECK HIM OUT!

HE'S TWICE OUR SIZE!

Uh-oh! As I suspected, lots of other males are here, too.

I SAW THEM FIRST!

NO, YOU DIDN'T.

Hopefully my whispy, white whiskers will catch their eyes — I've grown them specially.

It's worked! Some of them are coming over and that means it's ...

... DANCE TIME!

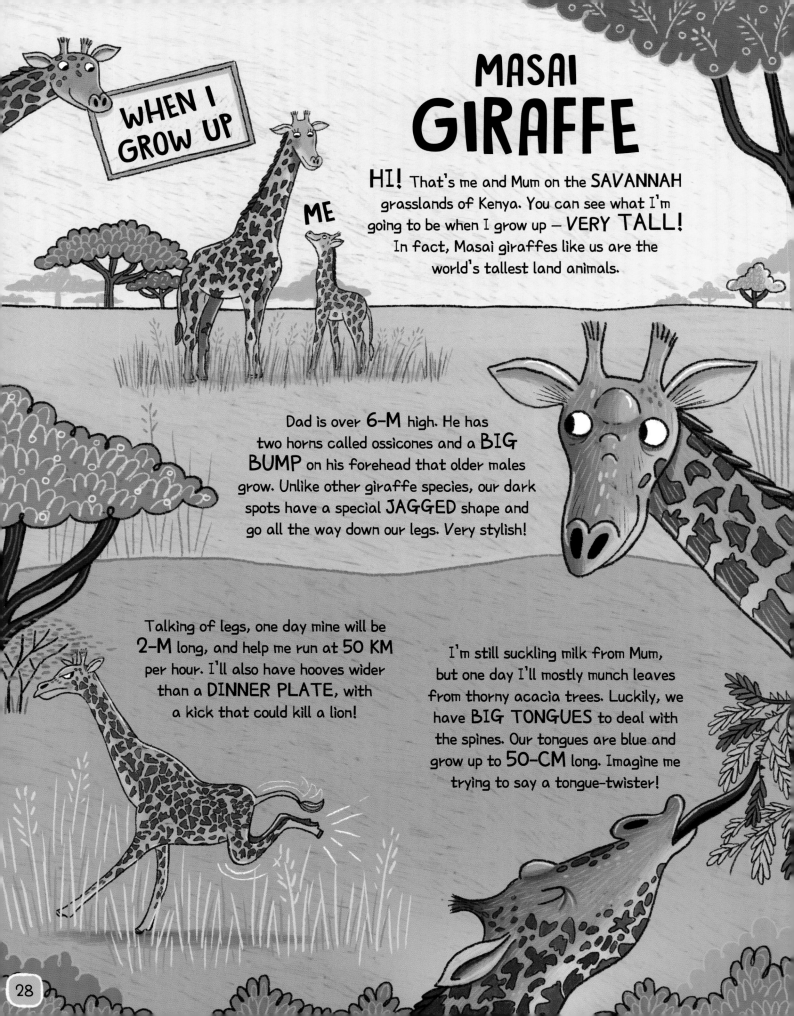

WHEN I GROW UP

ME

MASAI GIRAFFE

HI! That's me and Mum on the SAVANNAH grasslands of Kenya. You can see what I'm going to be when I grow up — VERY TALL! In fact, Masai giraffes like us are the world's tallest land animals.

Dad is over 6-M high. He has two horns called ossicones and a BIG BUMP on his forehead that older males grow. Unlike other giraffe species, our dark spots have a special JAGGED shape and go all the way down our legs. Very stylish!

Talking of legs, one day mine will be 2-M long, and help me run at 50 KM per hour. I'll also have hooves wider than a DINNER PLATE, with a kick that could kill a lion!

I'm still suckling milk from Mum, but one day I'll mostly munch leaves from thorny acacia trees. Luckily, we have BIG TONGUES to deal with the spines. Our tongues are blue and grow up to 50-CM long. Imagine me trying to say a tongue-twister!

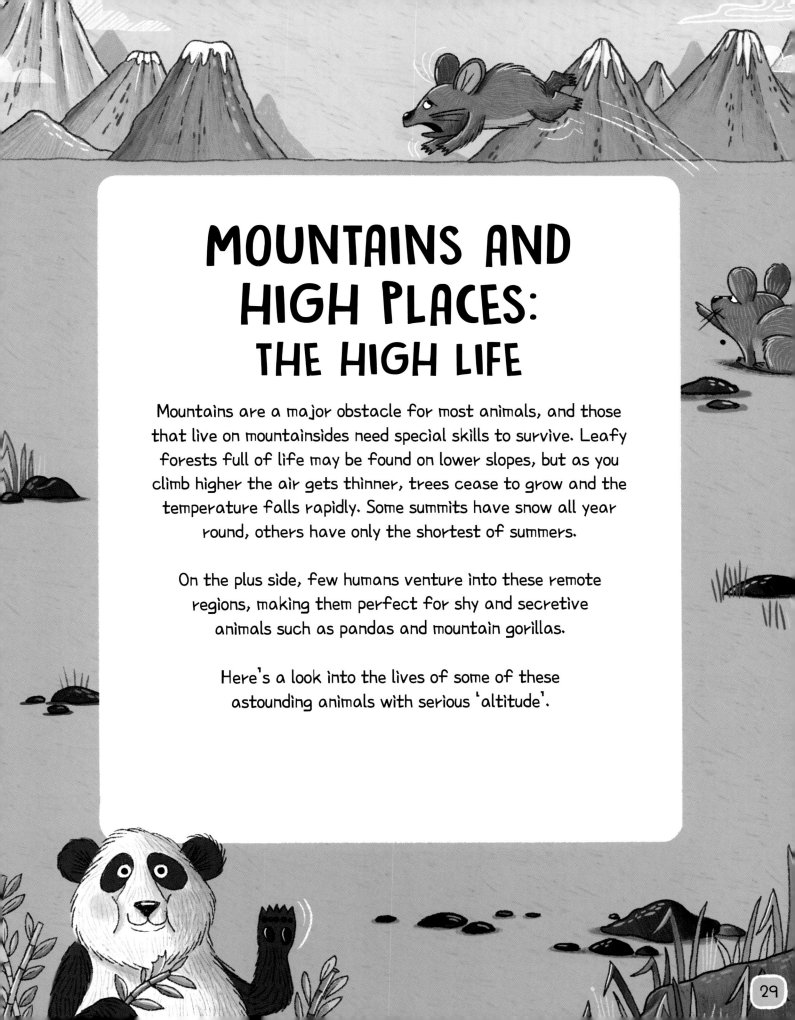

MOUNTAINS AND HIGH PLACES:
THE HIGH LIFE

Mountains are a major obstacle for most animals, and those that live on mountainsides need special skills to survive. Leafy forests full of life may be found on lower slopes, but as you climb higher the air gets thinner, trees cease to grow and the temperature falls rapidly. Some summits have snow all year round, others have only the shortest of summers.

On the plus side, few humans venture into these remote regions, making them perfect for shy and secretive animals such as pandas and mountain gorillas.

Here's a look into the lives of some of these astounding animals with serious 'altitude'.

HIMALAYAN PIKA

Hi! I'm a pika and I'm on top of the world — literally — on the slopes of the Himalayan mountains in Nepal.

I might look a bit like a hamster, but I'm actually related to rabbits. I have round ears, furry feet and no tail.

SOFT!

I'm only little, but I'm one of the world's highest-dwelling mammals, as this golden eagle knows only too well.

SWOOP!

LEAP!

EEK!

I spend a lot of time in rocky crevices — hiding from predators, sleeping and raising a family in the breeding season.

SAFE!

WILD STYLE

HIGH SOCIETY

Some of the planet's most secretive animals live on mountains.
Here are some styles that are top of the range.

JUMP TO IT!

The Himalayan jumping spider was discovered about 100 years ago, close to the summit of Mount Everest. Possibly the world's highest-living land animal, its hairy legs and body help it detect the tiny insects it eats.

BRIGHT BIRD!

The Alpine chough is a type of crow with a golden beak and bright orange legs. These birds live at high altitudes throughout Europe and Central Asia, and have learnt to follow mountaineers and beg them for food.

GIDDY GOAT

Ibexes, wild goats with spectacular curved horns, are found high up on mountainsides around the world. In the mating season, males fight with these heavy horns to see who is boss. Scary!

TREASURE CHEST

The gelada is a baboon-like monkey that lives in the mountains of Ethiopia, Africa. It has a bright-red, hourglass-shaped patch on its chest, giving it the nickname 'bleeding-heart monkey'.

SNOW LEOPARD

WHEN I GROW UP

ME

HI! I'm a snow leopard cub living with my brothers and our mum high on a MOUNTAIN in MONGOLIA. Mum says snow leopards mostly live alone when they are adults, so there's no dad around to stop me and my brothers practising our FIGHTING.

Mum says that one day I will have super THICK FUR and HUGE FURRY PAWS just like hers. Apparently, they will keep me from sinking into the 'snow', whatever that is. Luckily, us cubs are born in the summer.

COSY!

Mum's tail is MASSIVE — almost as long as her. It balances her body when she's hunting, and she can curl it over to keep her nose warm when she sleeps. Wake up, Mum, I'm hungry!

One thing I won't be doing when I'm bigger is roaring. Mum says that, unlike lions and tigers, we can't. Instead, I'd better start practising a really loud miaow.

MIAOWWW!

MOUNTAIN GORILLA

Oh, hello. We're a troop (group) of shy mountain gorillas hiding high up in the misty cloud forests of the Rwandan mountains in East Africa.

UH-OH, WE'VE BEEN SPOTTED.

It can get really cold up here, so we have longer fur than eastern lowland gorillas, our closest relatives.

MOUNTAIN GORILLA

LOWLAND GORILLA

Here is a female member of my troop checking me for fleas and dirt.

LEAP!

GROOM!

I need to keep well-groomed as I'm the big older male in charge of everyone. I'm known as a 'silverback', for obvious reasons.

I'M NOT GREY, I'M SILVER!

HA!

Younger males are called 'blackbacks'.

BLACK IS CLEARLY MORE STYLISH.

I AGREE!

There are also lots of babies in the group — all of them fathered by me.

I'VE GOT HIS EYES

ME TOO!

AND ME!

Just like human kids, they can be a bit of a handful at times.

BOUNCE!

PLAY WITH US!

SIGH!

And that's not all we have in common with you humans. We also don't like cold mornings.

And we don't like the rain.

In fact, we don't really like water at all.

What we do like is eating — lots!

Followed by sleeping and belching.

And then lots more eating, sleeping and belching.

Basically, though we may look big and scary, we're just salad-loving gentle giants who wouldn't hurt a fly. We're even afraid of caterpillars.

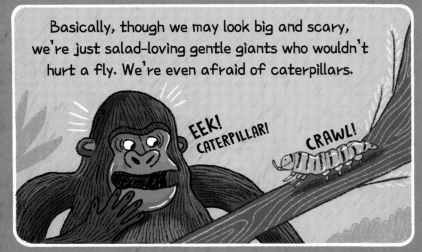

GIANT PANDA

Hi! I'm a cute and adorable giant panda. I live in a bamboo forest high in the mountains of Central China. Gimme five?

For me it's more like 'gimme six', as I have five claws plus a fake thumb to help me hold my favourite food. In fact, it's almost my only food ...

... bamboo — in all its delicious forms!

BAMBOO SHOOTS   BAMBOO LEAVES

I can even crush the stiff stems with my super-strong jaws.

BITE! CHOMP!

16 hours out of every 24, bamboo goes in one end of me ...

NOM! NOM!

... and up to 50 times every day, bamboo comes out at the other!

SOME PRIVACY, PLEASE!

PLOP! PLOP! PLOP!

It hardly changes. Look, you can still see green leaves in my poo.

That's because my guts are really rubbish at digesting bamboo. So to make up for it, I have to chomp and chew up to 30 kg of it day in, day out.

RUMBLE!
RUMBLE!

With predictable results!

PLOP!
PLOP!
PLOP!

(AGAIN.)

Every panda ideally needs a big bit of forest (about 115 km^2) to keep itself fed.

So we live alone and move slowly to save energy, with our thick fur helping to keep us warm.

Basically, we just eat, poo, eat, poo and sleep.

Oh, and every so often we stand on our hands to wee up a tree to scent-mark our territory.

It makes a nice change from eating and pooing.

SPLASH!

Yep, we sure are cute and adorable!

CHOMP!

ANDEAN CONDOR

Hi! I'm a male Andean condor perched on a mountainside in Chile. Want to watch me at work?

LEAP!

Okay, we have lift off!

I have a 3-m wingspan, making me one of the world's largest flying birds. I travel up to 100 km a day in search of food. And I have amazing eyesight.

SOAR!

GLIDE!

OOH! A DEAD LLAMA!

Er, you might want to look away for the next bit, but it's why I have a featherless head and a big hooked beak.

RIP!
TUG!
GUZZLE!
BZZZ!

Yes, I eat dead meat. It's a dirty job but someone's got to do it.

Eating corpses stops them rotting and spreading diseases, plus I preen to keep myself clean afterwards.

I'M KEEN TO PREEN!

Well, all except for my strange habit of pooing on my own legs!

PONG!
STINK!

When the poo dries out, it cools my legs down, but it sure does pong!

DESERTS: HOME AND DRY

Deserts are dry regions where rain is a rarity.
In fact, the definition of a desert is a place where
less than 25 cm of rain falls in an entire year.

Deserts can be found on every continent on Earth.
Many, but not all, are sandy — with the African
Sahara being the largest of these.

Typically, deserts are hugely hot in the day and
uncomfortably cold at night, making survival
a series of extremes for desert-dwellers.

Some animals hide from the heat and come
out at night. Others love the sun and seize
the day. Here are some of their secret lives.

MEERKAT

Hello! Welcome to our meerkat colony in Namibia, Southern Africa. Every one of us has a job to do — including me!

Below me, a team are using their long front claws to dig burrows for us to live in.

HEY! WATCH OUT!

Good job we can close our ears to keep out dust and dirt.

SCRAPE!

DIG!

PARDON?

Back up in the hot desert sun, I can see that others are busy babysitting and feeding the pups.

AND I'M NOT EVEN THEIR REAL MUM.

SUCKLE!

PLAY!

ME NEITHER ...

ERM, SO WHERE IS OUR MUM?

The pups' mum is the leader of our colony, known as the alpha female. Right now she's in charge of hunting for our favourite food, scorpions.

COULDN'T WE EAT SOMETHING LESS SCARY?

DON'T WORRY. YOU SIMPLY HAVE TO BITE OFF THEIR TAILS FIRST!

JUST YOU TRY!

WILD STYLE

HOME AND DRY

Sandy deserts are some of the most extreme environments on Earth. Here are some styles that are going down a storm.

A SIDEWAYS LOOK

The sidewinder rattlesnake of the Mexican desert has horn-like projections over its eyes that may act like sun shades. It also has some of the animal kingdom's hottest moves. It slides sideways, meaning less of its body comes into contact with the fiery desert sand.

DON'T MESS WITH MUM!

The deathstalker scorpion is found in deserts from Africa to the Middle East. Its curved, venomous stinger can twist to hunt prey from different angles. Females care for their babies by carrying them on their backs.

NARROW SQUEAK

Oddly oval, the desert rainfrog is found only on a short stretch of sandy coast in Southern Africa. It lies in damp sand to keep its skin moist and deters predators by inflating its body and squeaking like a chew toy.

SOLID GOLD

The fur of many golden moles matches the African desert sand they tunnel through. Totally blind, they detect the vibrations of insects above them and shoot up to grab them.

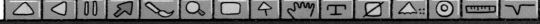

CACTUS WREN

Hello. We're a family of cactus wrens nesting in the hot Arizona desert. Watch yourself! Those spines are sharp.

It's nice inside though. We've lined our nest with lots of soft feathers. Come in and have a look.

See? Being in such a prickly place protects our young from prying predators, such as wolves and coyotes.

FEED ME! CHEEP! CHEEP!

The nest also faces into the wind to help keep it cool. It's hot here!

GUST!

BLOW!

We're not keen fliers, so we spend most of our time on the ground looking for insects. This is when it can also get rather dangerous.

EEEK! COYOTE!

YUM!

This is when a nice spiky cactus comes in handy yet again. Sharp!

NOPE!

COME OUT OF THERE!

HA!

In fact, cacti are such a good defence against predators, we even build decoy nests just to confuse them.

ANYONE AT HOME?

THORNY
DRAGON LIZARD

In the wide open Western Australian desert I appear ... A DRAGON!

Er, I'll just move out of the shade so you can see me better.

I'm actually a lizard you humans call a thorny devil. I look scary with my sandy-coloured spines, but really I wouldn't hurt a fly.

THAT'S GOOD TO HEAR.

IT IS!

Well, I might, but in fact ants are my favourite food.

EEK!

WHAT?

It's too hot for lots of walking about, so I just settle down in front of an ant trail and pick them off as they pass by.

YUM!

THIS IS SO UNFAIR!

(INDIGN-ANT!)

They're very more-ish.

HELP!

2,500 ANTS LATER

After all those ants, I could do with a drink. Only there's no proper water here in the desert.

Luckily I had a good drink in my burrow before I set out. I have special scales that can suck the moisture out of damp sand, like a sponge, and pass it to my mouth.

In fact, I think I'll head back there now. I warn you, this could take some time.

First, I freeze on the spot and do nothing, in case there are predators around.

STAYING STILL!

Still doing it, sorry!

STILL STILL!

Then I rock backwards and forwards.

SWAY!

ROCK!

Then — and only then! — do I take a step forwards. Now we're getting somewhere.

STEP!

But if there's any sign of danger I puff myself up, tuck in my head and present this 'false head' on my back as real.

Phew! 'False' alarm — but the idea is that a predator attacks that instead of my real head.

So, time to be on my way once more.

THERE WE GO ...

Nope, sorry. Frozen again. Er ... bye!

FENNEC FOX

Hi! We're a family of fennec foxes — the world's smallest wild dogs. We live in a burrow under the hot sand of the Sahara Desert.

Our kits (our young) weigh just 50 grams when they are born.

And they're very cute!

We hide from the hot sun during the day, then in the evening we head out from one our den's many entrances to hunt. Our burrows can be up to 10-m long!

I'VE POPPED OUT OVER HERE!

Our bodies are brilliantly adapted for desert life.

HOT STUFF!

SANDY-COLOURED FUR FOR CAMOUFLAGE.

HAIRY EARS HALF THE SIZE OF OUR BODIES. THEY ACT LIKE RADIATORS, PUMPING OUT HEAT TO KEEP US COOL.

BUSHY TAIL, USED FOR STEERING WHEN RUNNING.

FURRY FEET TO BEAT THE HEAT OF THE SAND.

SAND CAT

ME

HI! Cute picture, eh? That's me with my mum and sisters outside the entrance to our burrow in the MOROCCAN DESERT. Our coats match the sand, which I guess is why we're called sand cats. Mum is just a bigger version of us kittens, which means I'll still look young even when I'm older. Result!

In summer, it's so hot in the day that Mum hunts at night when it's cooler. One morning she came back with breakfast (a juicy jerboa!) and I was amazed she didn't leave any pawprints. Apparently, it's because we have FURRY FEET as protection against the hot sand.

NO TRACKS!

Mum also brought back a deadly VENOMOUS VIPER for us to eat. She says the trick is to HIT them hard with your paw, then bite them quickly on the neck. It sounds scary, but exciting — and they're tasty, too!

SLAP!

Sad news. It seems sand cats mostly live alone as adults, so I've been practising my DIGGING. One day — hopefully — I'll have kittens of my own and we'll need a new burrow to live in.

DIG!

POLAR REGIONS:
POLES APART

The North Pole and the South Pole are the coldest places on the planet. The Arctic region around the North Pole gets as low as -70°C in winter. The continent of Antarctica around the South Pole can fall to a frighteningly freezing -90°C.

Summers see 24-hour sunlight, but are over in days. Winters consist of constant darkness. It is too cold for trees, and soils stay frozen just below the surface. Despite all this, life survives in these extreme conditions.

Here are some of the coolest animals from our coldest regions.

MACARONI PENGUIN

Hi! I'm a female macaroni penguin swimming in the sea off the remote Atlantic Island of South Georgia, within the Arctic Circle. It's summer here and ...

SWIM!

... eek! Leopard seal!

LUNGE!

BITE!

SWERVE!

Sorry, as I was saying, it's summer — the breeding season — and I'm heading 500 km back to ...

SWIM!

LUNGE!

BITE!

SWERVE!

... HELP!
Orca!

Phew, that was lucky. I'm heading back to here — the same rocky island I raised a chick on last year.

Being so rocky, it's rather hard to get on to. What I need is a helpful wave ...

SPLOOSH!

... wahey! Who says penguins can't fly?!

WHOOSH!

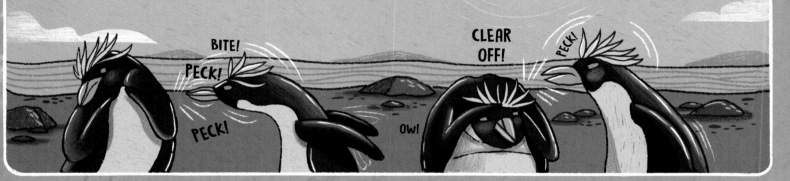

ARCTIC WOOLLY BEAR CATERPILLAR

Hello! Welcome to Greenland in June — it's the height of summer here. I'm a caterpillar of the Arctic woolly bear moth, and I'm greedy for grub!

CHOMP! CHEW! — ARCTIC WILLOW

I'm filling up on lots of plants because I have only a few weeks before the big freeze comes back.

CHOMP! MUNCH!

Thanks to thick snow, this bit of Greenland turns white for 11 months each year.

I spend that time literally frozen stiff inside a special cocoon hidden in the rocks. It can be as cold as -70°C.

FROZEN!

It's still pretty cold here even in summer, so between leafy feasts I sunbathe to warm up. Just a few more hours, then I should be done.

SHINE!

BASK!

I've been living life like this for seven years now.

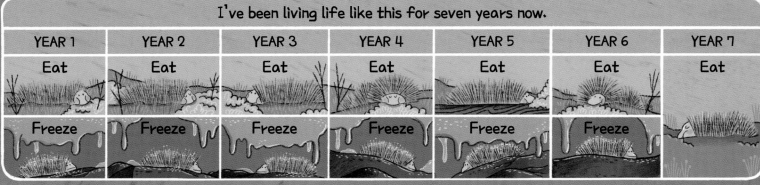

YEAR 1	YEAR 2	YEAR 3	YEAR 4	YEAR 5	YEAR 6	YEAR 7
Eat	Eat	Eat	Eat	Eat	Eat	Eat
Freeze	Freeze	Freeze	Freeze	Freeze	Freeze	

But now I'm finally large enough to make my last cocoon and then turn into a beautiful moth ... See you again soon!

After two weeks, I emerge. Pfft! I'm a boring grey colour. All those years for this? Oh well, I'm off to find a mate before the snow comes back. Bye!

FLUTTER! FLAP!

WILD STYLE

POLE STARS

Living within worlds that are white with snow for much of the year, here are some of the polar regions' seasonal looks!

DISH OF THE DAY

Arctic lemmings are an important food for many animals in the Arctic, including snowy owls and Arctic foxes. Luckily, lemmings have lots of babies, who soon go on to make lots more lemmings themselves. Shown here in its summer coat, in winter it will turn white for camouflage.

CLEVER FEATHERS

Rock ptarmigans are birds that live high on Arctic mountainsides. In summer their feathers blend in with the rocks and soil, while in winter they develop white ones to blend in with the snow.

OUT-FOXED

Acrtic foxes turn from grey to white in winter for camouflage. They have thick warm fur and use their large fluffy tails to keep themselves warm when they curl up to sleep.

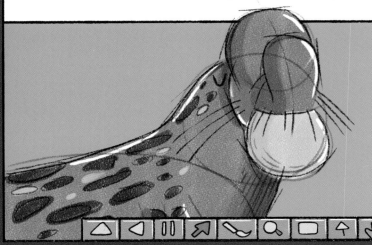

WHAT A BLOW!

Hooded seals swim in icy northern waters. Adult males have a strange bladder on their heads that they can inflate, plus a pink, balloon-like membrane they blow out of their left nostril. Both are used for display to attract females.

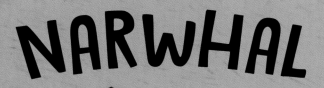

NARWHAL

Hi! We're part of a pod of odd-looking whales called narwhals.

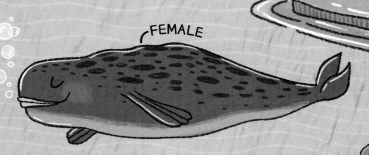

FEMALE

MALE

Winter and summer, the Arctic Ocean is our icy home.

We're the most northerly living whales in the world.

Males like me grow a twisted tusk, which is up to 3-m long. A tusk is actually a super-sized tooth!

A few females also grow a tusk though, but your scientists aren't quite sure what they're for.

We do know that you humans used to try to fool people into thinking our tusks were unicorn horns.

Occasionally, we do use them to stun tasty fish by hitting them.

SMACK!

OW!

Then we suck the floppy fish straight into our mouths! Delicious!

SUCK!

In winter we swim out to sea, far under the ice.

SWIM!

To find food, us males dive down vertically to look for fish on the ocean floor. It's the shortest route!

This means going for 20 minutes without coming up for air.

DEEP!

And we can do it 15 times a day. Gasp!

Luckily, we have squeezable ribcages that support our organs when going down deep.

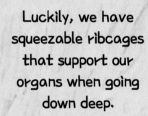

SQUASH!

PRESS!

I'm under a lot of pressure here!

ME TOO!

EEK!

Orcas and Greenland sharks like to lunch on us, but our biggest threat is from polar bears that lie in wait at our breathing holes. Hopefully, I'm safe heading up ...

NEED AIR! GASP! SWIM!

YUM!

YUM!

ANTARCTIC KRILL

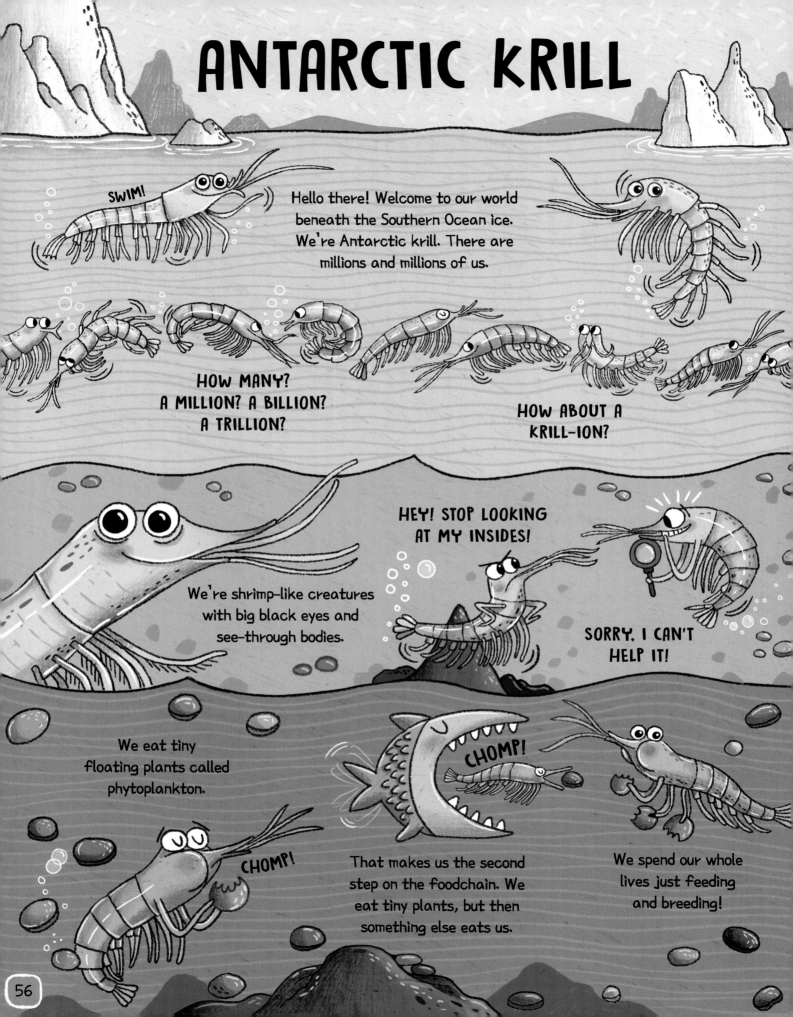

SWIM!

Hello there! Welcome to our world beneath the Southern Ocean ice. We're Antarctic krill. There are millions and millions of us.

HOW MANY?
A MILLION? A BILLION?
A TRILLION?

HOW ABOUT A
KRILL-ION?

HEY! STOP LOOKING
AT MY INSIDES!

We're shrimp-like creatures with big black eyes and see-through bodies.

SORRY, I CAN'T
HELP IT!

We eat tiny floating plants called phytoplankton.

CHOMP!

CHOMP!

That makes us the second step on the foodchain. We eat tiny plants, but then something else eats us.

We spend our whole lives just feeding and breeding!

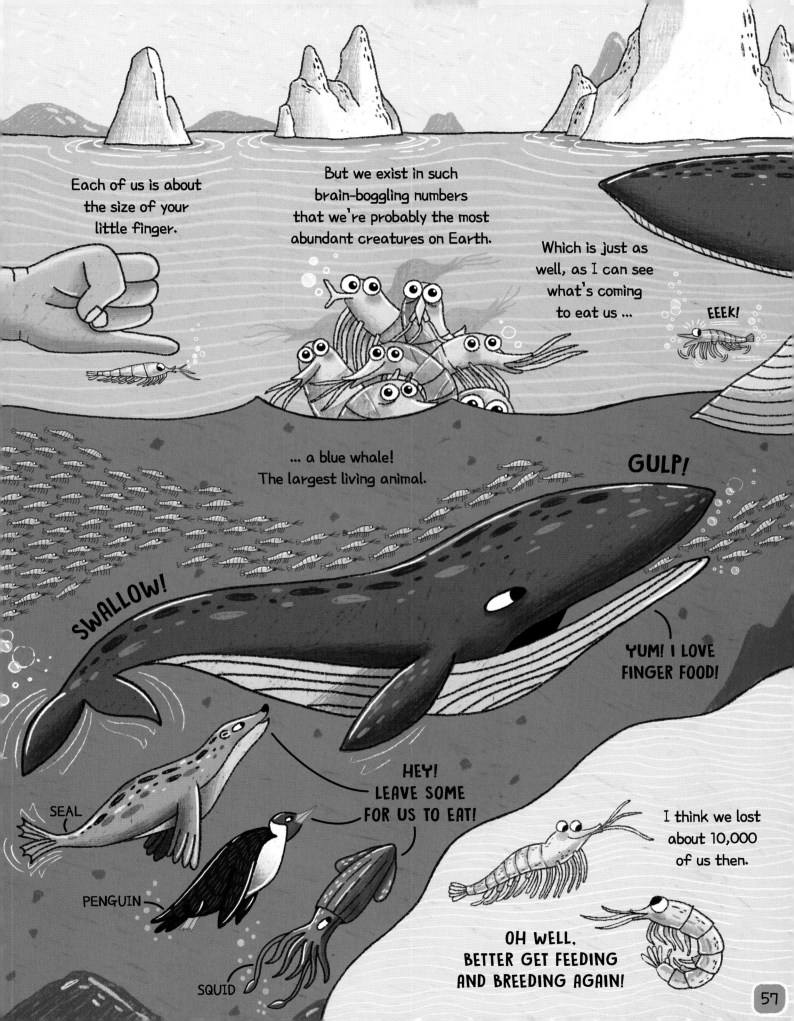

SNOWY OWL

ME

HELLO! Baby pictures can be so embarrassing. That's me and my brothers and sisters laying low in the Arctic tundra in northern Sweden. Summer has just ended and now everything is covered in snow — BRR!

The snow is why Mum and Dad have white feathers for **CAMOUFLAGE** in winter. I will, too, in a few months' time when I get bigger. Dad's feathers are whiter than Mum's. I already have their **BRIGHT YELLOW EYES**, which are among the largest of the owl species. We use them to spot our favourite foods — voles and lemmings.

Big feet are a big help when it comes to catching lemmings, as are huge, sharp **CLAWS**. Long **FEATHERS** keep our toes cosy in the cold, as I will do a lot of standing on the snow as an adult looking for lemmings. Did I mention they're my **FAVOURITE FOOD?**

Even as youngsters, we already swallow our food **WHOLE** — bones and all. Our tough tummies dissolve the meat, then we cough up pellets packed with bones and fur. Here's one I made earlier — **ENJOY!**

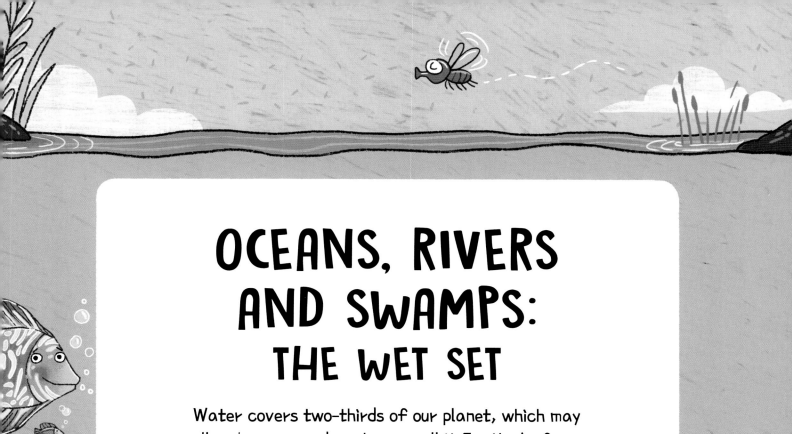

OCEANS, RIVERS AND SWAMPS:
THE WET SET

Water covers two-thirds of our planet, which may well make you wonder why we call it Earth. As far as we know, liquid water is essential for life, and only our little blue planet seems to have lots of it.

Almost all the water on Earth exists in our salty seas and oceans, with so-called 'freshwater' (non-salty) running in our rivers, streams and lakes, or locked up in our ice-caps and glaciers.

Life loves water. It started in water about four billion years ago, and today some of the world's wettest and most wonderful animals can be found in and around it.

ARCHERFISH

Our babies get together in shoals to practise shooting water accurately.

The babies also learn by watching us. We can even leap to pluck insects from the air.

We can blast water away from the stream bed to reveal worms and other food hiding in the mud.

But occasionally our shooting skills don't pay off, as another fish steals our 'hits'.

OLIVE SEA SNAKE

Hello! I'm an olive sea snake in a coral reef off the northern coast of Australia. I'm almost 2-m long. Don't believe me?

Well I bet you do now!

HELP! BIG!

I have a flattened tail that acts like an oar to propel me through the ocean.

I also have a short tongue that constantly tastes the water around me.

HMM, SALTY ... NO SURPRISE THERE.

It can be rough hunting over sharp corals, so I have protective overlapping scales, like tiles on a roof.

OOF!

SCRAPE!

Oh, and I almost forgot to mention, I also have the most toxic venom and my fangs are among the longest of any sea snake.

NOW YOU TELL ME!

Lucky for that clownfish I need to surface every few hours to grab some air.

SWOOP!

GASP!

EEK! Osprey attack — I'm off!

DIVE!

It's a lot safer down here.

NOT FOR US!

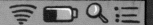

WILD STYLE

MAKING WAVES

The world's seas and oceans are home to an amazing range of animals. These four are watery wonders!

HEAVY HITTER

Mantis shrimp have super-sharp eyesight and fearsome front claws for locating, clubbing and spearing prey. They are so powerful they can actually smash the glass walls of fish tanks. They live in burrows in warm, shallow seas.

SHELLSHOCK!

Horseshoe crabs have shells the shape of horses' hooves. But their closest relatives are actually spiders, not crabs. They have blue blood, enjoy swimming upside down and date back to way before the time of the dinosaurs!

HERE BE DRAGONS!

The leafy seadragon is a wonderfully wavy type of fish found off the coast of South Australia. Disguised as drifting seaweed, it swims along slowly, sucking up prey through its long, trumpet-like snout.

BEAUTIFUL BUT DEADLY

Sea slugs, or nudibranchs, are related to the slugs found in gardens. Many have bright colours to warn predators they are poisonous, while some have similar markings simply to pretend they are poisonous.

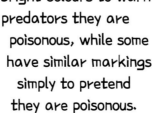

SOUTH ASIAN RIVER DOLPHIN

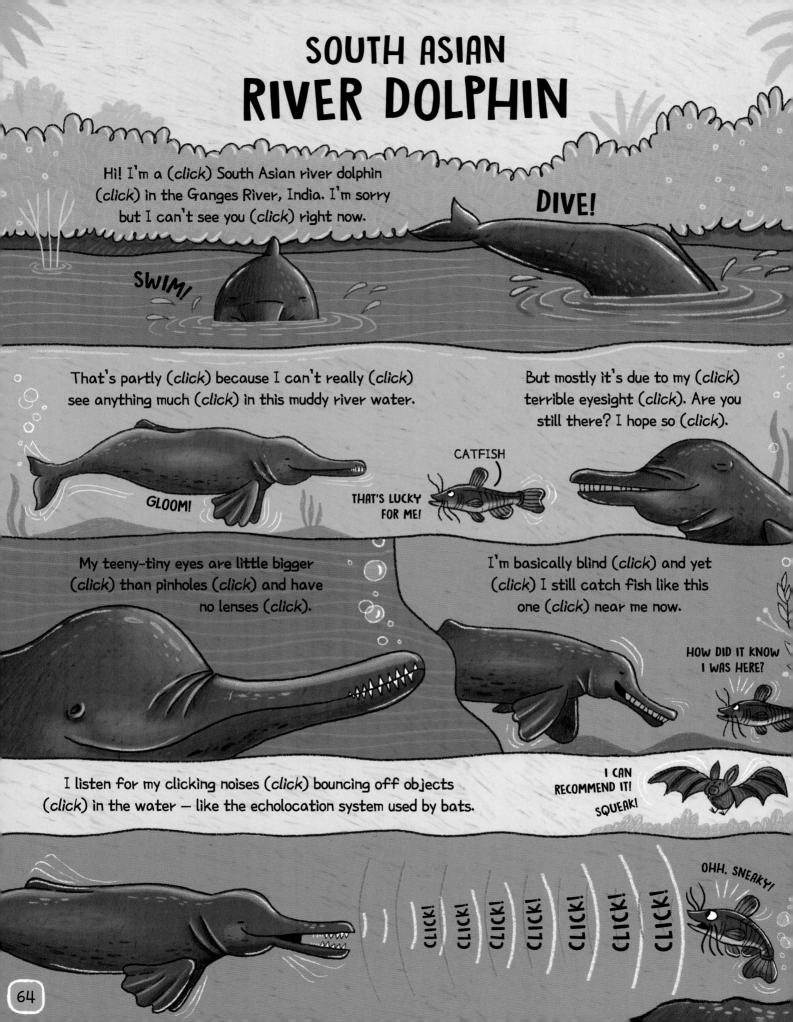

Hi! I'm a *(click)* South Asian river dolphin *(click)* in the Ganges River, India. I'm sorry but I can't see you *(click)* right now.

DIVE!

SWIM!

That's partly *(click)* because I can't really *(click)* see anything much *(click)* in this muddy river water.

But mostly it's due to my *(click)* terrible eyesight *(click)*. Are you still there? I hope so *(click)*.

CATFISH

GLOOM!

THAT'S LUCKY FOR ME!

My teeny-tiny eyes are little bigger *(click)* than pinholes *(click)* and have no lenses *(click)*.

I'm basically blind *(click)* and yet *(click)* I still catch fish like this one *(click)* near me now.

HOW DID IT KNOW I WAS HERE?

I listen for my clicking noises *(click)* bouncing off objects *(click)* in the water — like the echolocation system used by bats.

I CAN RECOMMEND IT!

SQUEAK!

CLICK! CLICK! CLICK! CLICK! CLICK! CLICK! CLICK!

OHH, SNEAKY!

GREEN BASILISK LIZARD

Hi! I'm a green basilisk lizard soaking up some rays in a forest in Costa Rica, Central America.

SOAR!

EEK!
A cunning eagle.
Sorry, must run.

SWOOP!

And I do mean RUN! Even on water.

ZIP!

ZOOM!

SPLASH!

I have special toes on my back feet. They have fringes of skin that spread out in water and increase the surface area of my feet.

This means I can run on the surface at over 20 km per hour.

SPLISH!

SPLASH!

SPLOSH!

SPLOOSH!

But sadly only for a few metres. Er, ever get that sinking feeling?

SINK!

SLIDE!

Luckily, I'm also a very good swimmer so I should make it safely back to land.

THAT'S WHAT YOU THINK.

SWIM!

CAIMAN

DISCUS
FISH

WHEN I GROW UP

ME

HELLO! Here's me and some of my hundred or so siblings after hatching from tiny eggs about two weeks ago. We are clinging to a rock in a warm, dark pool in a flooded **BRAZILIAN RAINFOREST**. We are literally small fry now, but we'll be a lot larger one day!

See what I mean? Aren't our mum and dad **BEAUTIFUL**? We are called discus fish because we are **FLAT** and **ROUND** like the discus thrown in athletics, but a lot more colourful.

Unusually for fish, Mum and Dad look after us as babies. For two weeks now, we've been **MUNCHING** on the **MUCUS** they make on their bodies. They take turns, flicking us between them when they've had enough. I wonder if it tickles to be nibbled like this?

Soon Mum and Dad will **SWIM OFF** when we try to feed on them, meaning we'll munch on plants instead. They will then rejoin their shoal of a dozen beautiful buddies and, one day soon, I'll have a **COLOURFUL CREW** of my own to feed. I can't wait!

VAMPIRE SQUID

Hi! I'm a vampire squid living 600-m deep in a tropical sea. It's dark down here, let's turn on some lights.

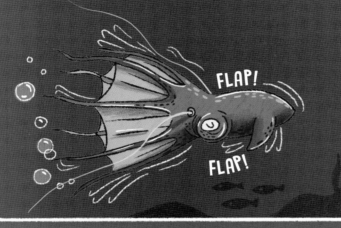

FLAP!
FLAP!

GLOW! SHINE!
SHINE! GLOW!

Ha! Did that startle you? I hope so. It's meant to.

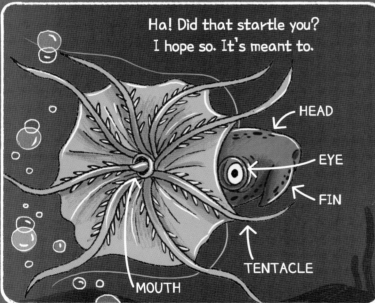

HEAD
EYE
FIN
TENTACLE
MOUTH

Here's one of my tentacles. I've got special light organs in my skin called photophores to scare off predators such as whales.

GLOW!

PHOTOPHORES
SUCKERS
SPINES

You humans call me a 'vampire' but I don't suck blood — I eat 'marine snow', tiny dead organisms that I catch on two sticky filaments, which look like threads.

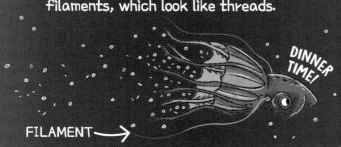

DINNER TIME!

FILAMENT →

Frankly, blood sounds tastier. Here's how I got my name. Watch this — one, two, three ...

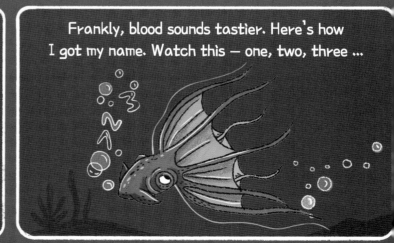

WHUMP!

Pretty clever, EH?

I can whip my tentacles back and forth over my head like Dracula flipping his cloak.

I do it as a clever defence mechanism against predators. And here's another one ...

SQUIRT!

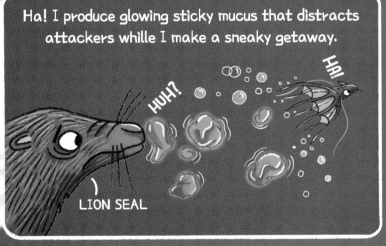

Ha! I produce glowing sticky mucus that distracts attackers whille I make a sneaky getaway.

HUH?

HA!

LION SEAL

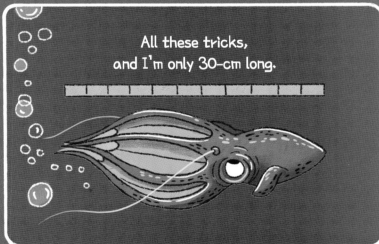

All these tricks, and I'm only 30-cm long.

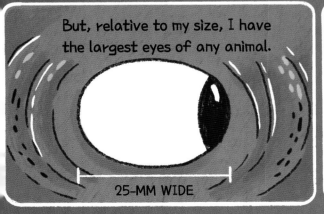

But, relative to my size, I have the largest eyes of any animal.

25-MM WIDE

Not that there's anything worth seeing down here. Apart from me of course.

SHINE!

GLOW!

69

PARADOXICAL FROG

Hi! Welcome to my pond in the Amazon Rainforest. You humans call me a paradoxical frog.

A 'paradox' is something that doesn't seem to make sense.

For example, I'm a frog, but when I croak I make a noise like a pig!

OINK! OINK!

But that is not how I got my name.

Check out this baby picture.

Look! As a tadpole, I was four times bigger than I am now!

7-CM LONG

Us paradoxical frogs have the world's largest tadpoles.

28-CM LONG

When I grew up, I actually got much smaller — that's the paradox!

HI, DAD! WHO YOU TALKING TO?

NO ONE YOU KNOW!

TELL ME!

GULP

NOCTURNAL AND DARKNESS: DARK SECRETS

At any moment in time, half the surface of our planet is cloaked in darkness. There are also caves, caverns and deep ocean depths where the sun's rays never reach, but life still exists and thrives.

Animals active at night are known as nocturnal. (Animals active in the daytime are called diurnal.)

For some animals, the lack of light is a wonderful way to stay safe. For others, sight is a sense they no longer need or rely on. These creatures of the night include many of the oddest animals on the planet. We shine a light on some of them here.

GREATER BULLDOG BAT

Hi! I live in a cave near a cove in
Costa Rica, Central America.

Inside, as night falls, I
wake up on one of its walls.
I've just been hanging
around here all day.

CLING.

STRETCH!

YAWN!

FLAP!

I'm a greater bulldog
bat — named because
my face reminds you
humans of one of your
breeds of dog.

But it's not just good
looks we have in common
— I also enjoy crunching
bones. Let's go fish!

That's right, I live close by the water,
because fish forms a big part of my diet.
First, I fly low and slow over the surface.

FLAP!

GLIDE!

FLAP!

Next, because it's dark and my eyes are tiny, I use echo-detecting skills to register ripples on the water made by fish.

SQUEAK!

SQUEAK!

SPLASH!

RIPPLE!

My giant ears pick up the echoes of my high-pitched squeak, helping me pinpoint a target.

HMM.

Then, I lower my super-long legs and dip my huge hooked claws just below the water's surface.

SWOOP!

CATCH!
EEK!

The fish never know what hits them!

Then I take off. You could call my fishing technique 'splash and grab'.

SUCCESS!

I eat mid-flight and fill my cheeks with chewed-up food. Is it rude to squeak with your mouth full?

Then I go back for more.
Bye!

GREAT POTOO

Can you spot me? I'm on a branch of a dead tree in a rainforest in Venezuela, South America.

Take a closer look.

Closer ...

... okay that's close enough, thank you.

Yes, I'm a nocturnal bird called a great potoo and this is what I do all day — impersonate a tree stump.

I'm not asleep, I'm watching you through the little gaps in my eyelids.

I can use them to see behind me, too.

Now go away, and come back when it's dark.

Hmm, that was quick. Well now you can see just how big my eyes are.

THEY'RE MAHOO-SIVE!

And, as this tasty beetle is about to find out ...

HELP!

... my mouth is even bigger!

DOOMED! EEK!

And that's how I spend my nights — eating ...

... and making the occasional call.

BWAAAAAR

BYE!

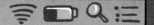

NIGHT SIGHT

Many animals spend their lives under the cover of darkness. Here we meet some of these shadowy characters.

SHARK IN THE DARK

Greenland sharks live in the lightless depths of the icy Arctic Ocean. Some have been discovered to be over 400 years old, many are blind and they are very slow swimmers. Their eyes are replaced by parasites that glow in the dark, attracting fish for the shark to eat.

YOU SMELL!

Kiwis are the national bird of New Zealand. Flightless, they have wings that are useless (as they're so tiny) hidden under a coat of hair-like feathers. They also have a long beak ending in a pair of super-sensitive nostrils, which help them hunt by smell at night.

HOT SPOT

Pit viper snakes are found across the world. They have special heat-detecting organs in pits on either side of their heads that allow them to hunt their prey in darkness, using just the warmth of their victims' bodies.

EYE-SPY

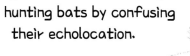

Named after the moon, the luna moth flies at night, probably to avoid insect-eating birds. Its large green wings have eyespots that are thought to confuse predators. Similarly, the long 'tails' on its hindwings may mislead hunting bats by confusing their echolocation.

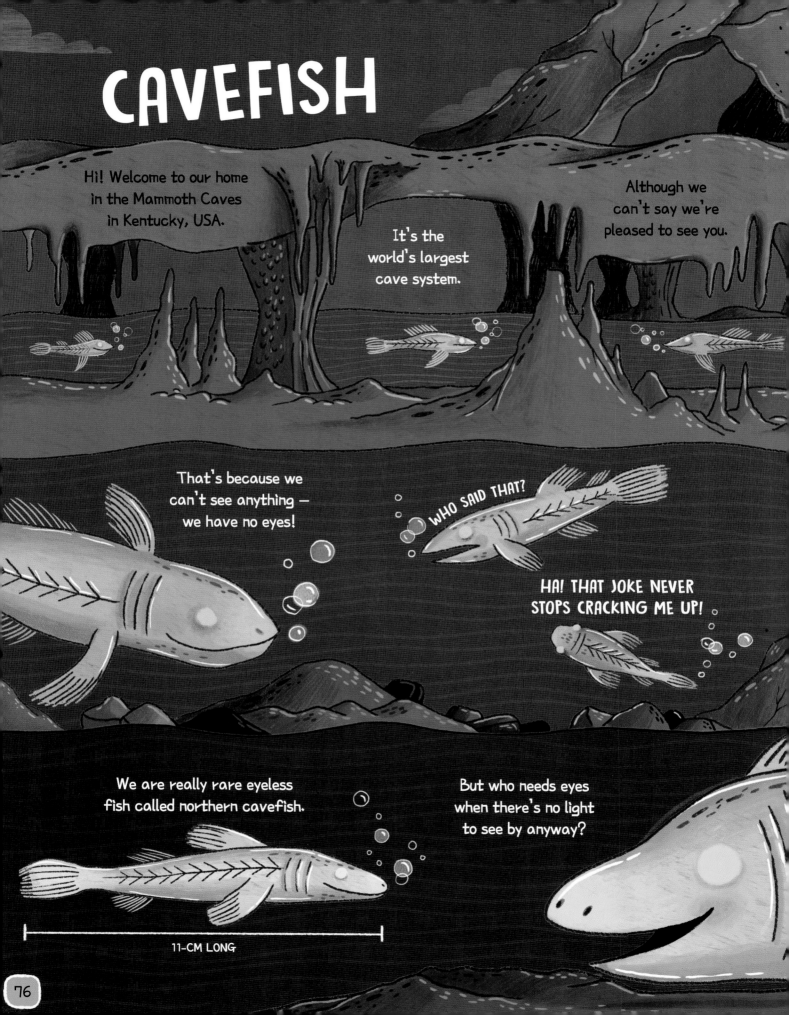

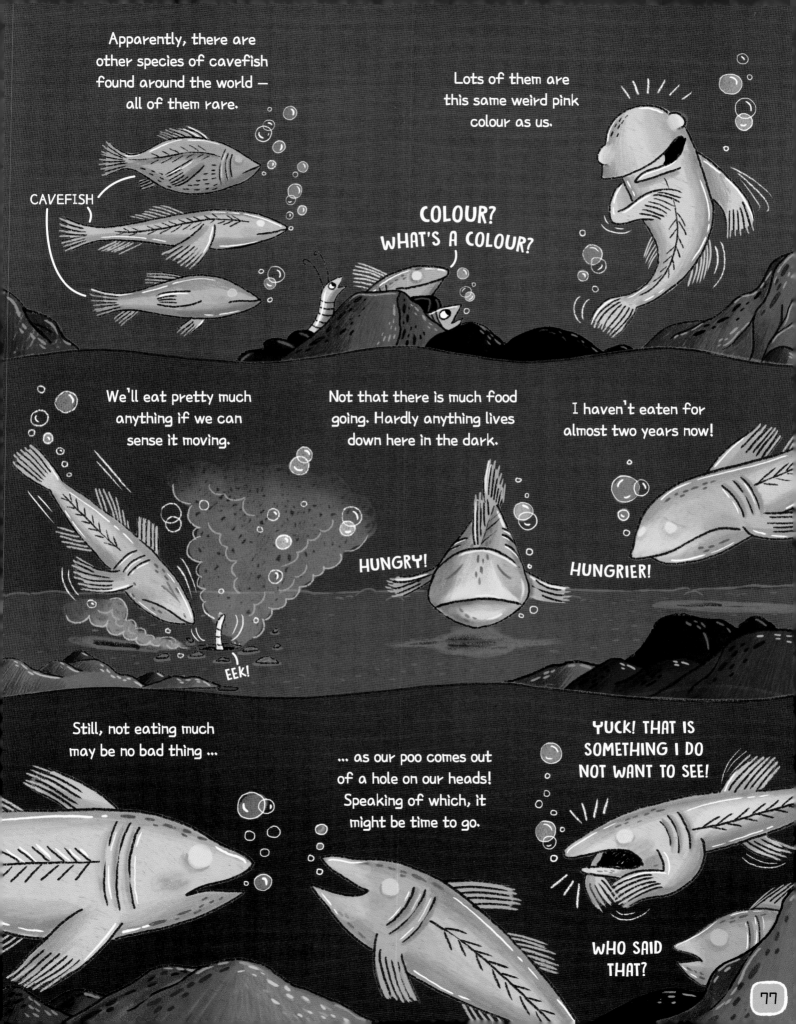

AYE-AYE

WHEN I GROW UP

ME

HI! I'm a baby aye-aye — a type of lemur living in the treetops of a **MADAGASCAN RAINFOREST**. Right now, my fur is silver with a big black stripe down my back. But it won't stay that way for long.

Here's Mum foraging for **FOOD** in the canopy. One day, I'll have dark fur and a **BIG, BUSHY TAIL** like hers. I already share her **HUGE EARS**. They'll help me detect food when I switch from her milk to hunting grubs.

TAP! TAP! TAP!

Here's how she does it. Us aye-ayes have **LONG, CURVED FINGERS**. The middle one is **SUPER-THIN** and she uses it to **TAP** on branches, listening for echoes. Hollow branches can contain yummy grubs that she catches by chewing through the bark and winkling them out with her skinny fingers.

Home right now is a big ball of leaves and branches where we spend the day. Mum heads out to hunt when the sun starts to set. One day, I'll build a home of my own just like this one. For now though, this aye-aye is saying 'BYE, BYE'.

78

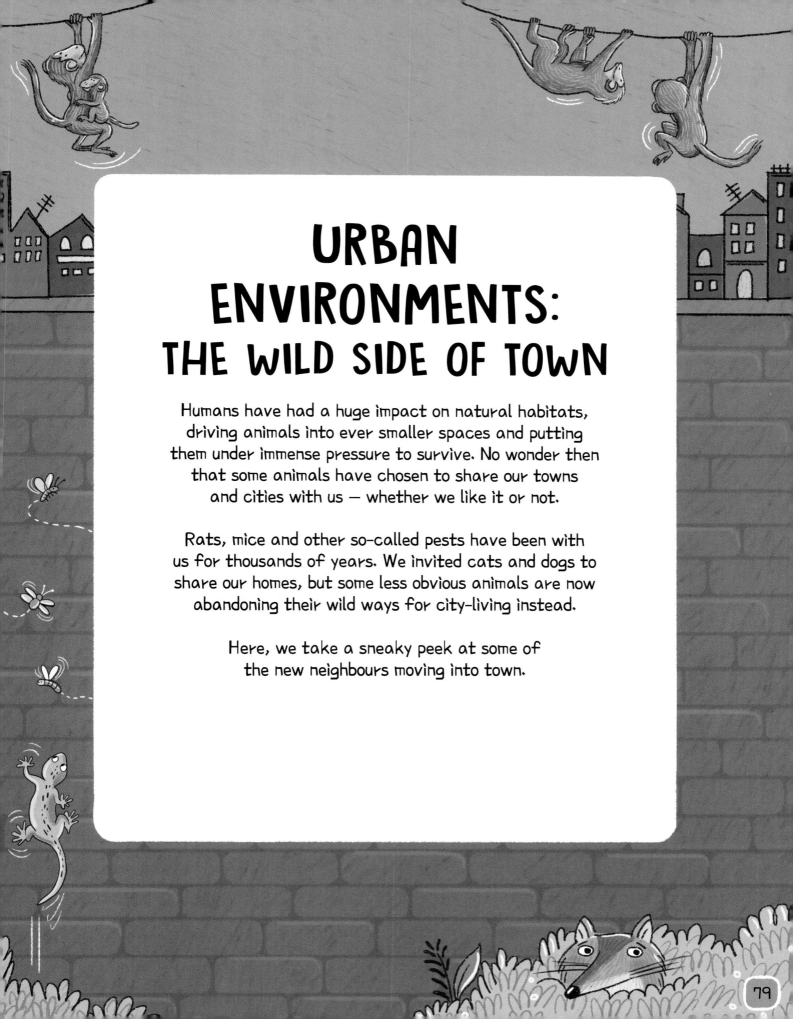

URBAN ENVIRONMENTS:
THE WILD SIDE OF TOWN

Humans have had a huge impact on natural habitats, driving animals into ever smaller spaces and putting them under immense pressure to survive. No wonder then that some animals have chosen to share our towns and cities with us — whether we like it or not.

Rats, mice and other so-called pests have been with us for thousands of years. We invited cats and dogs to share our homes, but some less obvious animals are now abandoning their wild ways for city-living instead.

Here, we take a sneaky peek at some of the new neighbours moving into town.

RHESUS MACAQUE

Hi! Welcome to Jaipur in India. I'm an adult rhesus macaque — a type of monkey found across Asia. Me and my troop live here in a holy temple on the outskirts of the city.

YOU CAN SAY THAT AGAIN!

THE HUMANS CONSIDER US SACRED!

BUT WE CAN BE BADLY BEHAVED.

People that visit the temple can feed us with small bags of food they buy with a donation.

But we also like to vary our diet.

HELP!

FANCY A CHANGE?

YES! NUTS TO THESE NUTS!

So each day we go into town for a takeaway.

TOWN CENTRE!

There can be 50 or more of us!

And when I say 'takeaway' ... well, you'll see what I mean.

As soon as we hit the city, we scale its heights using our incredible climbing skills.

Our hands and feet can grip like human hands!

CLIMB!

GRIP!

Our forward-facing eyes mean we are great at judging distances. Once we're all up on a roof, we make death-defying leaps between tall buildings.

Our long tails help to balance our bodies.

JUMP TO IT!

HURRY UP!

LEAP! JUMP!

We can also hang like acrobats from the many power cables that criss-cross the city.

Though occasionally we might get a shock!

SWING!

DON'T SLIP MUM!

ZAP!

But it's you humans who get the shock when we 'takeaway' your food from under your noses.

BREAD ... SWIPE!

EVEN PIZZAS!

FRUIT ... SWIPE!

SWIPE!

90 per cent of our diet in Jaipur is made up of food we steal from humans.

Us macaques are making monkeys out of you!

CHOCOLATE COOKIES ARE MY FAVOURITE!

MINE TOO!

EUROPEAN MANTIS

Hello, I'm an insect called a mantis. Welcome to my favourite spot in the garden of a house in Portugal.

You humans call this a rose bush, but I call it a waiting room.

That's because I sit here all day waiting with my front legs raised as if I am praying.

And I wait ...
BUZZ!

... and I wait.
BUZZ!

And sometimes I turn my head to look right behind me.
TURN!
I CAN SWIVEL.

And then I wait some more.

And then at last ...
LAND!
SMELLS NICE!

... I pounce!
HELP! EEK!

Spiny claws mean my prey can't escape. Then I eat it alive.
GULP! BYE!

Talking of being eaten alive ...
UH OH!
LAND!

Luckily, my impressive threat display usually scares them off!
FLASH!
BYE!

82

ME — WHEN I GROW UP

RED FOX

Hi! Here's me and my brothers and sisters outside our home in the garden of a human house in a big British city. We live in a DEEP HOLE dug by our mum called an EARTH. Foxes are big on digging, so I've already been practising.

We are also geniuses at JUMPING. Mum and Dad can easily clear the 2-m-tall fence around the garden. Us little kits (babies) keep practising when we play, but we're not that good — yet!

LEAP!

Our BIG BROTHERS and SISTERS from last year's litter help Mum and Dad look after us. They bring us things to eat such as rats, mice, pigeons, earthworms and — best of all — BIN FOOD: stuff humans have thrown away. Hopefully, next year I'll also be helping Mum raise her next lot of kits.

It's fun being in a big family, and there's another family I hope to meet soon: the HUMANS whose food we eat and who watch us from their windows. Who needs the countryside? BYE!

RED OVENBIRD

Hi! Welcome to our home high above the city of Brasília, Brazil.

We're a pair of red ovenbirds. But the name doesn't mean we're keen to be cooked.

No, it's because we're reddish-brown in places.

And our nest looks like a clay oven you humans might use. But we don't build our nests in trees ...

... they're on utility poles!

Lots of us live up here, and we don't even mind the traffic that much. Though it can get very noisy.

SHHH!

HONK!

HONK!

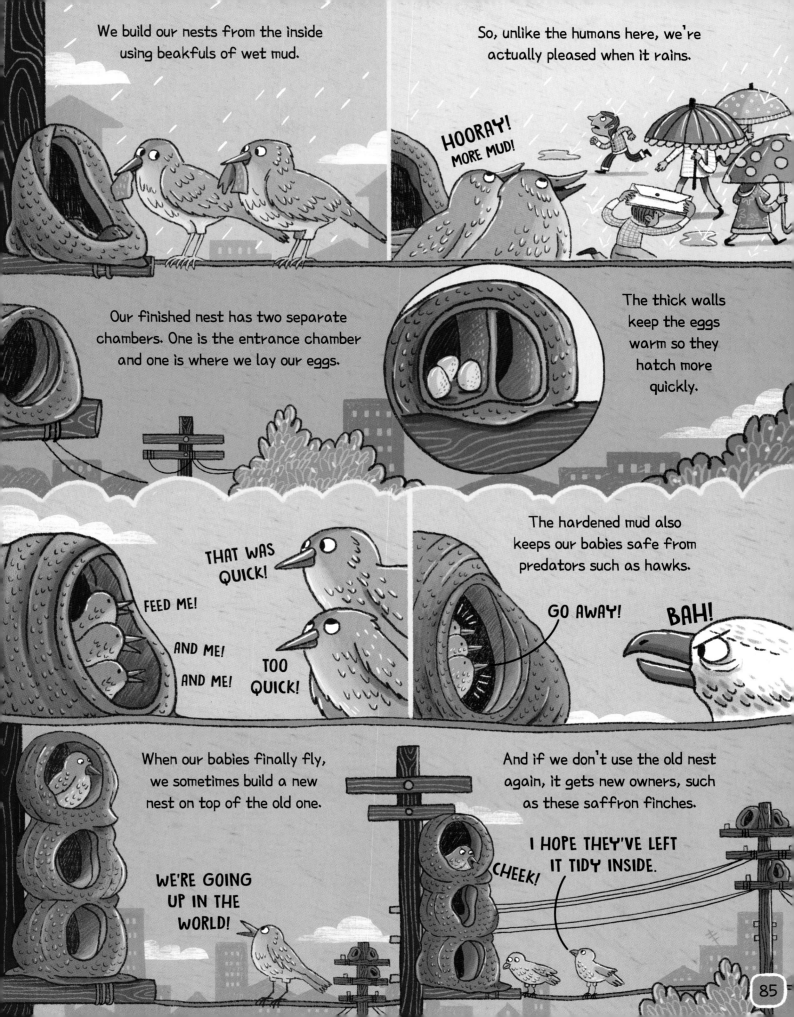

We build our nests from the inside using beakfuls of wet mud.

So, unlike the humans here, we're actually pleased when it rains.

HOORAY! MORE MUD!

Our finished nest has two separate chambers. One is the entrance chamber and one is where we lay our eggs.

The thick walls keep the eggs warm so they hatch more quickly.

THAT WAS QUICK!

FEED ME!

AND ME!

AND ME!

TOO QUICK!

The hardened mud also keeps our babies safe from predators such as hawks.

GO AWAY!

BAH!

When our babies finally fly, we sometimes build a new nest on top of the old one.

WE'RE GOING UP IN THE WORLD!

And if we don't use the old nest again, it gets new owners, such as these saffron finches.

CHEEK!

I HOPE THEY'VE LEFT IT TIDY INSIDE.

COMMON HOUSE GECKO

Hello! Welcome to our lovely home in Kuala Lumpur, Malaysia.

I'M A COCKROACH.

I'M A WASP, AND WE JUST WANTED TO SAY ...

... GOODBYE!

GRR!

EEK!

The cheek of these insects! Can't they read? This is all about me. I'm a type of small lizard called a common house gecko.

And here's the common, quite ordinary sort of house I share with those insects and some humans.

And here's my 'home-within-a-home' — a crack in the wall where I hide in the day, keeping safe and out of sight.

But at night, when it gets dark, I come out and start climbing the walls ... literally.

I can go up ...

SCUTTLE!

... and up ...

RUN!

CLING!

... and up!

I can also move sideways ...

SCAMPER!

STICK!

HOLD!

Frankly, I'm a pretty wizard lizard.

... and I can even hang upside-down on the ceiling.

What makes the magic happen? Well, you have to hand it to my feet! For a start, they're big and flat.

All five toes on all my four feet have tiny microscopic hairs on their soles. This means they can stick to any surface.

Even glass!

Us geckos choose to live with you humans because at night your lights attract the insects we love to eat.

SHINE!

YUM!

I taste the air with my tongue. I'm excited to eat those moths, beetles and bugs already!

FLICK!

However, there are some unwanted guests we hate having to share our house with.

EEK! A CAT!

LEAP! GRAB! HELP!

BREAK!

Phew! Managed to escape by shedding my tail!

TWITCH!

Luckily I'll grow a new one eventually. Bye!

WILD STYLE

URBAN JUNGLE

With humans increasingly invading natural habitats, here are some top trendsetters moving into our world.

FAST FASHION

Once rare in the wild, peregrine falcons have thrived in many big cities thanks to a plentiful supply of pigeons. By folding their wings, the falcons can catch prey mid-air at 320 km per hour — making them the fastest animal on Earth.

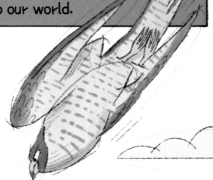

TAKING THE BISCUIT

Sika deer have spots for camouflage. However, they can be easily seen in the Japanese city of Nara, begging for biscuits in the local park. They have also learned to bow their heads to ask for food.

WHAT A BOAR!

Baby wild boars have cute stripes that help keep them hidden in plants and shrubs. Despite this, their parents bring them through the busy streets of the German city of Berlin, where there is a breeding population of over 3,000 boars.

WHAT A STAR!

Starlings get their name from the little star-like flecks on their chest feathers. They thrive in cities and in winter form massive flocks called murmurations that swirl through the sky at dusk.

AMERICAN BLACK BEAR

Hi! I'm an American black bear living in a forest in California, USA.

We're the world's most common bears and are found all across North America. But we're not all black.

I'M A GLACIER BEAR FROM ALASKA, USA.

I'M A CINNAMON BEAR FROM COLORADO, USA.

I'M A SO-CALLED 'SPIRIT BEAR' FROM CANADA.

It's autumn here in the forest right now, and I have an un-bear-able need to feed.

HUNGRY!

That's because I'm about to spend all winter in a cosy den in a deep sleep called hibernation.

ZZZZZZZ

Frankly, I'll eat pretty much anything — acorns, berries, roots, shoots — to build up body fat. I'm nuts about nuts!

PICK!

YUM!

I'll even smash open trees to raid the honey-filled nests of wild bees.

CLAW!

STING!

But for bears like me that live near humans, there's an even sweeter treat available.

This food is found in your gardens, and comes in cans ...

CLICK! OPEN!

... rubbish cans!

YUM!

How could you throw this away? It's delicious!

CHOMP! MUNCH!

We also like turning your bird feeders into bear feeders.

EEK!

Plus we really enjoy eating at some of the finest restaurants. Well, outside them anyway.

JOE'S CAFE

Yes, us bears have you humans beaten 'paws down'.

We have better hearing ...

GET OUT OF THE BIN, BEAR!

UH-OH!

... better eyesight ...

OOH, HE LOOKS ANGRY.

SHOO!

... and luckily we can run faster, too.

RUN!

There's just one thing I wish I could do the same as you humans — read!

WARNING!
BEARS ACTIVE IN THIS AREA

I wonder why this bin won't open? Bye!

100% BEAR-PROOF

GLOSSARY

Here are explanations of some words you may have read while meeting the animals in this book.

ADAPTATION
How a species changes its behaviour or body to suit its environment.

ALPHA MALE OR FEMALE
The male or female which has the highest rank in the animals' social group.

ANTENNAE
Long organs on the heads of some insects and spiders, which are used to help them sense their environment.

CAMOUFLAGE
A tactic or defence mechanism that animals use to disguise their appearance, usually to blend in with their surroundings and hide from predators.

CANOPY
The dense layer of trees and branches that are found at the top of the rainforest.

COLONY
A group of animals of one species that live together and interact closely with each other.

DESERT
An area of land which receives little rain, making it a hard environment for animals to survive in.

ECHOLOCATION
A technique which animals, such as bats and dolphins, use to find their way around and locate objects and prey. They do this by producing sound waves that bounce back off anything they hit.

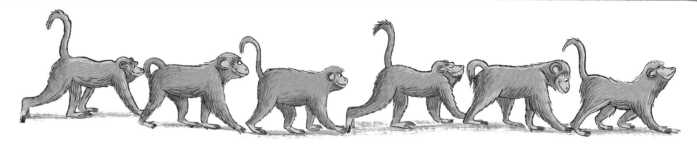

FOREST

An area which is covered in trees. Rainforests are tropical forests in areas that receive a lot of rain.

GRASSLAND

An area where the plant life is dominated by grass.

HABITAT

A place in the natural environment where an animal makes its home. Deserts and forests are two examples of habitats.

LARVAE

The early stage of development some animals, such as insects, go through.

MAMMAL

A warm-blooded animal with hair or fur. Mothers feed their young on milk.

MARSUPIAL

A type of mammal which isn't completely developed when born, and so is carried around in its mother's pouch. The wombat is an example of a marsupial.

MATING RITUALS

A set of behaviours that an animal, generally a male, goes through in order to attract a mate. These range from loud calls to showing off complicated dance moves.

NOCTURNAL

Animals that are active during the night, when they hunt and feed, and sleep in the daytime. (Animals that are active during the day are diurnal.)

PARASITE

A living thing that lives on or inside another living thing. It depends on this other living thing for food.

PREDATOR

An animal that lives by killing and eating other animals.

PREY

An animal that is killed by other animals for food.

SCENT-MARKING

A form of animal communication whereby an animal deposits its smell, for example by weeing or pooing in a particular place. It is mainly used for animals to mark their territory and to warn other animals to stay away.

SUMMIT

The highest point of a mountain or hill.

THREAT DISPLAY

Something an animal does to scare off other animals. This could include raising its legs, changing colour or making itself look bigger.

TUNDRA

Large, treeless areas found in cold regions where it's hard for plants to grow.